Snow White

First published 2008 by Brown Watson
The Old Mill
76 Fleckney Road
Kibworth Beauchamp
Leicester
LE8 0HG

ISBN: 978-0-7097-1823-9

Printed in Belgium

Snow White

Brown Watson

There was once a cruel Queen who was as vain as she was beautiful. Every day she would stare into her magic mirror and ask:

"Mirror, mirror on the wall,
Who is the fairest of them all?"

The mirror always replied:

"In all the land, 'tis you, oh Queen,
You are the fairest to be seen."

Now the
wicked
Queen
had a lovely
stepdaughter,
called Snow
White, who
was becoming
ever more
beautiful with
each day that
passed.

At last came the
time came when the
mirror announced:

"No maiden was more fair than thou,
But Snow White is the fairest now."

Furious, the cruel Queen summoned
her huntsman and ordered, "You must
take Snow White deep into the wild
forest and there you must kill her.
Then bring me her heart to prove that
you have obeyed me."

Meanwhile, Snow White
was talking to the deer and
birds in the palace gardens,
happy and completely
unaware of what had
happened.

Soon Snow White and the huntsman were riding out into the forest. Snow White was singing cheerfully and the huntsman was becoming ever more aware that he would not be able to kill this sweet child.

Finally he decided to tell her the evil Queen's plans.

"Now run away," he said,
"Deep into the forest where
the Queen will never find you."

The huntsman killed a deer and took its heart back to the Queen, telling her that it belonged to Snow White.

Meanwhile, absolutely terrified that the Queen might find her, Snow White rushed away through the trees as fast as she could, as deer, rabbits, squirrels and birds watched and followed her.

At last Snow White came to a clearing where a little cottage stood. Exhausted, she fell fast asleep on several little beds there. This was the home of the seven dwarfs. When they came home they were amazed and a little frightened to find Snow White there. She looked like a giant to them.

Snow White awoke and
when she told them
why she had run away,
they begged her to stay
with them.

She soon settled in
happily, singing as
she cleaned, cooked,
sewed and cared
for the dwarfs.

The dwarfs adored Snow White and she was delighted to have found such a lovely new home.

Meanwhile, the Queen decided it was time to talk to the magic mirror again. She could not believe her ears when the mirror sneered:

"At the Seven Dwarf's cottage, in the forest so green.

Snow White grows fairer than she's ever been."

Steaming with fury, the Queen
set out to find Snow White.
Soon she was knocking at the
cottage door, disguised as an
old lady.

"Please can you give a poor
soul a drink?" she asked,
offering Snow White a beautiful
rosy apple.

"Of course – and thank you,"
said Snow White,
taking a bite . . .
but the Queen had poisoned
the apple. Snow White gasped
and dropped to the ground.

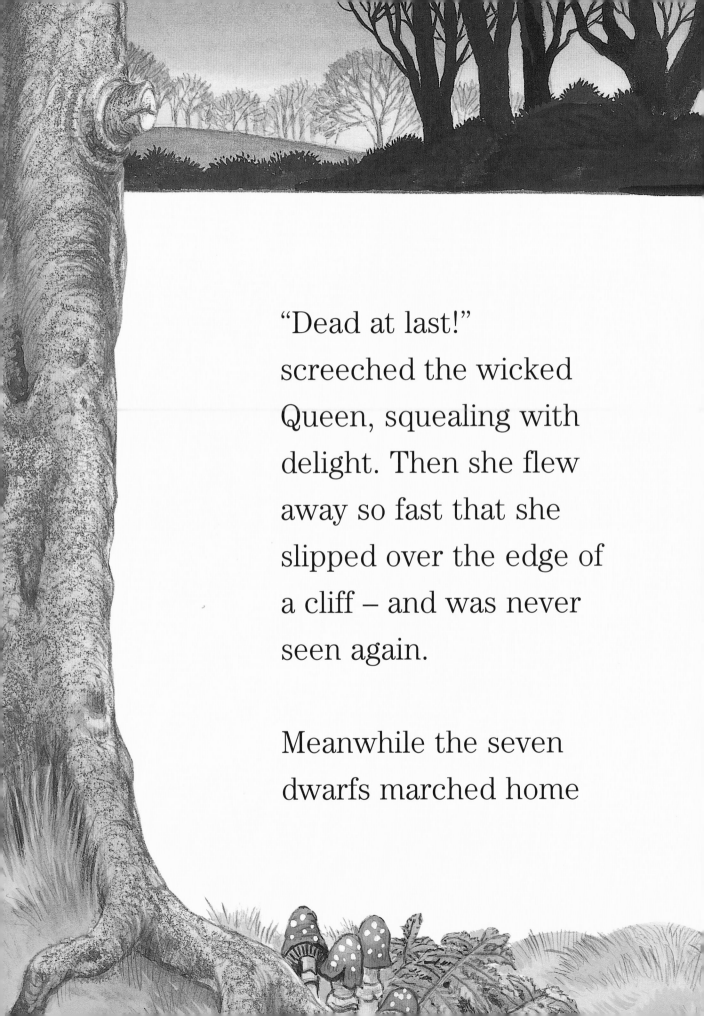

"Dead at last!" screeched the wicked Queen, squealing with delight. Then she flew away so fast that she slipped over the edge of a cliff – and was never seen again.

Meanwhile the seven dwarfs marched home

from their day
working in the
mines. They
were absolutely
broken hearted
to discover
Snow While
lying, apparently
dead, outside
the cottage.

The dwarfs placed their beloved Snow White to rest in a glass coffin, surrounded by the flowers she adored. They watched over her day and night.

What the dwarfs did not realise was that Snow White was still alive. She had not swallowed the piece of apple but its poisoned enchantment had left her deeply asleep.

Then
one bright
summer's day a
handsome prince
rode by. He stopped
to look at Snow White
and immediately fell in
love with the sweet princess.

As the prince leant over to
kiss her, the magic poison
vanished at last.

Snow White awoke and the fine young
prince took her into his arms.

The dwarfs clapped and
cheered, dancing with glee.

The Prince and Snow White were
married soon after. All the dwarfs
came to the wedding, dressed in fine
silk breeches and grinning from ear to
ear. They danced many a merry jig and
raised many a brimming glass to toast
the radiant bride and groom – who,
of course, lived happily ever after.

About this story

Most versions of this fairy story come from the Brothers Grimm collection of folk tales. Jakob and Wilhelm Grimm began gathering and rewriting German folk tales in about 1807. *Snow White and the Seven Dwarfs* includes a cruel stepmother but, in fact, their first version tells of a jealous mother – not a stepmother – who wanted to harm the princess.

Who is in this story?

Snow White is very pretty, with skin as white as snow, lips red as blood, and hair as dark as rich ebony wood.

The Wicked Queen is beautiful but vain and very jealous of Snow White. She can disguise herself in many ways. Her **talking mirror** is almost like a person, too.

...ack in the 1500s, small ...ildren who worked in the ...ines in one German town ...ere called dwarfs.

...n Albanian version has ...now White living with ...agons, not dwarfs, while ...e poem written in 1833

by Russian writer Alexander Pushkin introduced a group of knights instead.

Snow White was the story chosen by Walt Disney for his first full-length animation movie in 1937.

...e Seven Dwarfs ...ese kind little ...lk live in a cottage ...eep in the forest ...d work hard all ...y in the nearby ...amond mine.

... the Walt Disney ...ovie they were ...lled Bashful, Doc, ...opey, Grumpy, ...appy, Sleepy ...d Sneezy.

The Huntsman is frightened of the Queen but does not want to hurt Snow White.

The handsome **Prince** falls in love with Snow White and rescues her with a kiss.

Quick Quiz Questions

1

Add the missing word: "Mirror, mirror on the _ _ _ _."

2

What creatures can you see in the palace garden?

3

Where does the huntsman leave Snow White?

4

What does the huntsman take back to the Queen?

5

What becomes Snow White's new home?

6

What fruit does the
Queen poison?

7

Where does the
Queen fall?

8

Is Snow White
really dead?

9

Snow White's coffin is
made of _ _ _ _ _.

10

What flowers are in
Snow White's
wedding posy?

Answers

1

Wall

2

A deer, bird and rabbit

3

Deep in the forest

4

A deer heart

5

The cottage of the seven dwarfs

6

A rosy apple

7

Over the edge of a cliff

8

No, just enchanted and deeply asleep

9

Glass

10

Pink and gold roses